What Kind of Dog is That?

By

Elana J. Weinstein

Illustrated by

Steve Goad

LUMINARE PRESS
WWW.LUMINAREPRESS.COM

What Kind of Dog is That?

Printed in the United States of America

Luminare Press
442 Charnelton St.
Eugene, OR 97401
www.luminarepress.com

LCCN: 2023916457
ISBN: 979-8-88679-380-2

For Scott, my lifelong editor
and captain of the early morning
and late evening walks.

For Arielle and Trevor,
whose wisdom and dogged persistence
brought Dozer into our lives.

And of course, for Dozer, my inspiration
and my cuddly companion.

Hi there! My name is Dozer and I live on a road called Bow Wow Road. No, really, I do! I'm told that the name of the road comes from the time when Chief Konkapot and the Mohican Native American tribe lived in the area. I've only lived on Bow Wow Road for six years but it is the perfect place for a dog like me. What do I mean when I say a dog like me?

BOW WOW ROAD

Well, I am multicolored — gray, white, and brown — and my fur is very scruffy. I have distinguished eyebrows, a mustache, a beard, and big brown eyes. People ALWAYS like to guess what kind of dog I am, and that is a long story, but first let me tell you about my road.

On my road there are rabbits to chase, flowers to smell, sticks to chew on, birds to watch, and countless trees to sniff. My road is beautiful all year long so it is hard to choose which season is my favorite. In the fall, I love to hike in the nearby mountains as much as I can. I could hike for hours, feeling the leaves crunch under my feet, climbing the cool rocks, and best of all, looking out at the view from the top of the trail.

In the winter, I love to bury my nose in the freshly fallen snow, and feel the soft powdery flakes on my back. My feet are soothed by the cool blanket beneath them, and the crisp cold air gives me lots of energy! When we get back inside from a long walk, I like to curl up in a ball on my cushion and doze peacefully. (After all, I have to live up to my name!)

The spring brings spectacular smells and I feel happy because everything is waking up. I don't know which flowers I like more — the daffodils, tulips, crocuses, hyacinth, lilacs, globe flowers, or irises. And I can't forget the cherry blossom trees, which not only smell delicious but also cheer up the entire neighborhood with their bright pink blooms.

Summertime is when I get to spend the most time outside. I love to lie in the sun, and to feel the grass tickle my nose. On hot days I find shade on the screened-in porch, and let the smooth concrete floor cool my skin. Best of all are the sunsets, when the sky turns pink and orange, and then I can watch the fireflies light up the night. Oh and I almost forgot — I get to go on lots of car rides. I especially like it when the driver rolls down my window and I am allowed to stick my head out and feel the sun on my face and the wind in my fur.

Yes, Bow Wow Road is a pretty great place to live for a dog like me. I know, I promised to tell you what I mean by "a dog like me." I will, I promise! But first I have to tell you about some of the neighbors on my road.

There are plenty of nice people around, but I like to visit with the many other animals as often as I can. There is a nearby farm where I can see my friends, the cows and the horses. One horse always walks over to greet me, bowing his head in welcome. That same farm has goats, chickens, guinea hens, and my absolute favorite, the ducks! I really like chasing the ducks. For some reason they always run away from me though. I can't figure out why.

Besides all of those animals, there are also many dogs on the road. Well, it is called Bow Wow Road after all! At the beginning of the road is my friend Logan, the Jack Russell terrier. I can count on him to run out and say hi and he is always ready to share the news of the neighborhood with me. My next door neighbor on the road is Bella, who is a Black Labrador; I don't see her that often but every time I do I smile.

Then across from my house is a Welsh Corgi named Watson. I absolutely must come out and say hi every time he walks by because we like to jump and play together until his short legs get too tired. And then a little farther down the road is Jagger, a Dutch Partridge dog. He mostly lives outside or in the barn, and he is very lucky because he has lots of green fields where he can run. He also has his very own dog pool — what a lucky dog!

There are even more dogs on the road who I haven't met yet, but none of them can be described as "a dog like me."

You see, I am pretty unique! In fact, the question my family is asked the most when we are out for walks is "What kind of dog is that?" I am not exaggerating when I tell you that they are asked that question *every...single...time.* People seem to want to categorize me into just one type, but the thing is, I am many types. I am proud that I am a mixture of many breeds.

My family didn't know details about my background because they rescued me from an animal shelter in New York state when I was 9 months old. I am originally from Texas, near the city of Houston, and I traveled a long way to get to the shelter — 1,656 miles! I liked the shelter because I had many friends there but I was even happier when my family came to adopt me. I liked them right away, and the boy who was closest to my size seemed really excited to meet me. I looked into his eyes and I knew that I would be happy in my new home.

But back to the question of what do I mean when I say "a dog like me?" When my family came to the shelter and met me, they were told that I was a terrier mix. They were satisfied with that description, but since they kept being asked "what kind of dog is that?", they decided to find out more about my genes.

So are you finally ready to hear what kind of dog I really am? Here it is: I am 50% Schnauzer, 12.5% Basset Hound, 12.5% Parson Russell Terrier, 12.5% Labrador Retriever, and 12.5% Chihuahua! My family jokes that I have the beard, mustache, and eyebrows of a Schnauzer, the eyes of a Basset Hound, the fur of a Parson Russell terrier, the body type of a Labrador Retriever, and the vocal personality of a Chihuahua!

All of these types mixed together make me who I am! So I guess you could call me a Schnassetlabterhuahua! It has a nice ring to it, don't you think? It reminds me of one of my other favorite words — supercalifragilisticexpialidocious. (You can ask someone in your family what that means.)

I love that I can't be narrowed down into one type of dog; that makes me special. Just like people — they have many traits and characteristics that make up who they are. I think their differences are what makes life interesting! The way I think about it, every day is a new opportunity to notice different things, smell different smells, and most importantly, try different treats! Thanks for hearing my story and for letting me share a little bit about who I am. Ask your family what makes you different, and when you find out, celebrate how special YOU are!

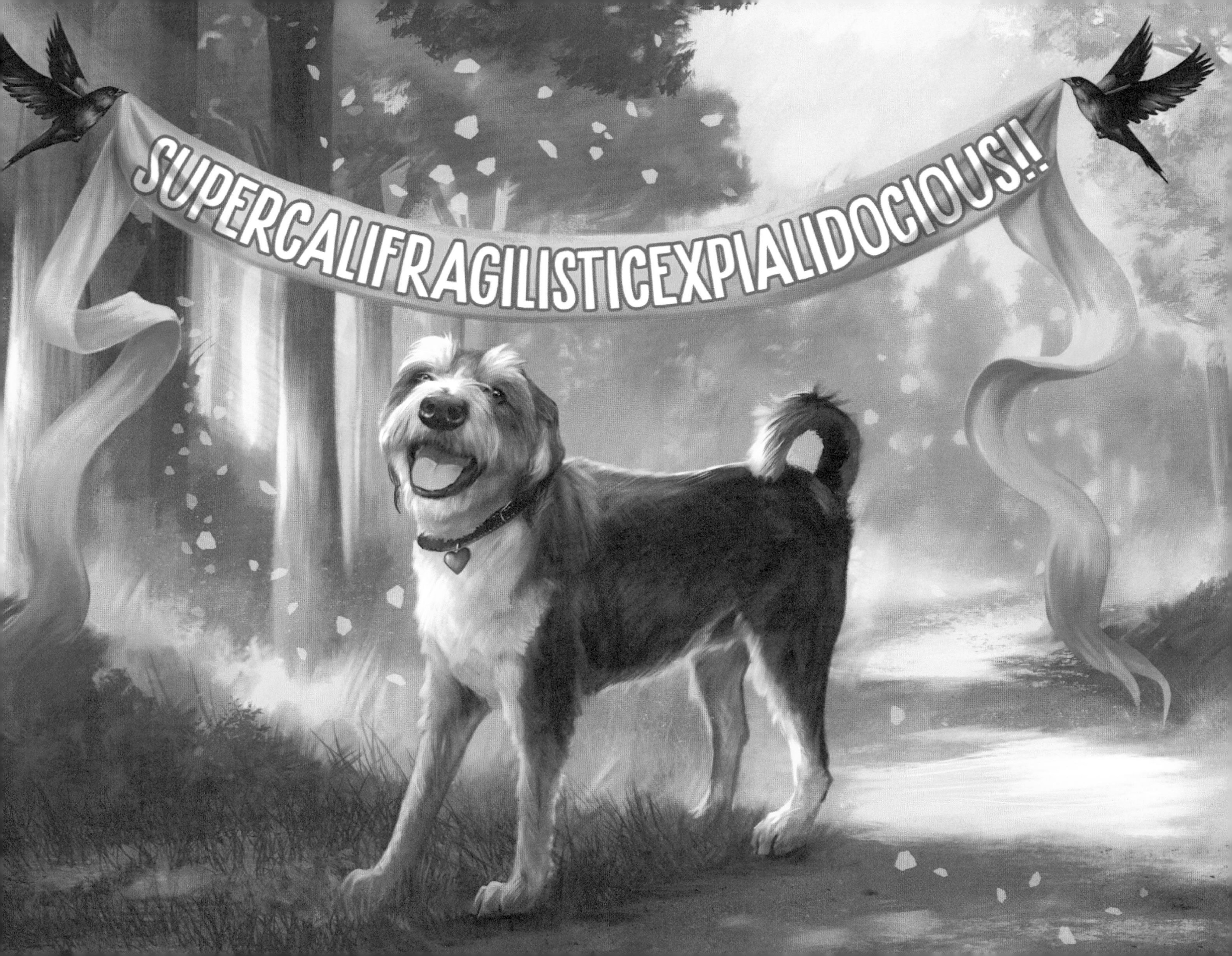
SUPERCALIFRAGILISTICEXPIALIDOCIOUS!!

About the Author

Elana Weinstein makes her debut as a children's book author with *What Kind of Dog is That?* In addition to writing, she is passionate about theatre, music, skiing, running, and crossword puzzles. She is also an amateur lyricist. Elana is a native New Yorker who splits her time between Manhattan and Massachusetts with her family and, of course, her dog, Dozer.

About the Illustrator

Steve Goad is an artist specializing in digital and traditional mediums. His works include a range of subjects that have been featured in film, video games, documentaries, magazines, books, and album covers. He lives in the Black Hills of South Dakota with his wife and his dog, Saluki.